What Rhymes with Sneeze?

D0272955

First published 2012
by A & C Black, an imprint of Bloomsbury Publishing plc
50 Bedford Square, London WC1B 3DP

www.acblack.com

www.poetryzone.co.uk

Text and collection copyright © 2012 Roger Stevens
Illustrations copyright © 2012 Spike Gerrell

The right of Roger Stevens and Spike Gerrell to be identified as the author and illustrator of this work has been asserted by them in accordance with the Copyrights, Designs and Patents Act 1988.

ISBN 978-1-4081-5576-9

A CIP catalogue for this book is available from the British Library.

All rights reserved. No part of this publication may be reproduced in any form or by any means – graphic, electronic or mechanical, including photocopying, recording, taping or information storage and retrieval systems – without the prior permission in writing of the publishers.

This book is produced using paper that is made from wood grown in managed, sustainable forests. It is natural, renewable and recyclable.The logging and manufacturing processes conform to the environmental regulations of the country of origin.

Printed by CPI Group (UK), Croydon, CR0 4YY

What Rhymes with Sneeze?

Roger Stevens

A & C Black • London

For Jill, with love

LONDON BOROUGH OF WANDSWORTH	
9030 00002 3264 1	
Askews & Holts	03-May-2012
C821.92 STEV	£4.99
	WWX0009239/0019

CONTENTS

INTRODUCTION

Welcome to *What Rhymes With Sneeze?* And if you said *breeze*, *cheese* and ABCs – you would be right!

But did you know that *snacks*, *snoring* and *snow* also rhyme with *sneeze*? Not to mention *tweet*, *weave* and *meal*. Even *pies* and *lazy* rhyme! This book will explain why.

If you'd like help writing your own rhyming poems you'll find lots of tips along the way – as well as a closely guarded secret: a technique used by professional poets to make their rhyming poems sound... well... professional. That's on page 71.

So prepare to find out lots of fascinating information about rhymes and rhyming. Of course, if you don't want to know all this and just want to read some poems – that's great too. I've included around sixty of my own favourites here as well as several great rhyming poems from some other poets.

Oh, and one more thing. To get the very best out of poems you should read them aloud. If you read the poems in this book out loud you'll hear how the rhymes work, and feel the rhythm of the poem.

Best fishes*

Roger

*Rhymes with *wishes*

What is Rhyme?

That seems like a straightforward question, doesn't it? But the answer's not so simple. The most basic rhyme happens when two similar words share the same end sound but begin with a different sound – such as *sneeze* and *cheese*, or *verse* and *worse*. And you'll find lots of poems in this book that use rhyme in this way.

But one of the things that makes poetry so interesting are the many variations on this theme. For example, what happens when you add an extra syllable to one of the rhyme words? (You get a **half rhyme** as in *bend* and *ending*.) Or what if the rhyme seems to work but doesn't quite, as in *thumb* and *one* or *green* and *fiend*? (This is called a **forced rhyme**.)

You can also rhyme the beginnings or middles of words, but I'll tell you more about this as we go along.

When two lines of verse end with the same word – that's *not* a rhyme. *Sneeze* does not rhyme with *sneeze*! You can have an identical rhyme though, as in *bare* and *bear* – these are different words with different letters, even though they have the same sound.

Rhyme Schemes

A rhyme scheme is simply the way poets organise their verses: how they decide which line will rhyme with which. Poets use the alphabet to explain the rhyming pattern, putting the letters in the order of the lines of the poem:

a = the first sound
b = the second sound
c = the third sound
and so on.

The most common way to rhyme poems is to rhyme the second and fourth lines of a verse (this is called an **a b c b** rhyme).

In the first verse of my poem *First Out of Class* the words that end each line are *classroom* (**a**), *queue* (**b**), *one* (**c**) and *two* (**b**). *Queue* and *two* rhyme so they are both **b**.

First Out of Class

I am the first out of the classroom	**a**
I am first in the dinner queue	**b**
I am standing at number one	**c**
And you are at number two	**b**

But Jill has to go to gym club
So I let her go in front of me
So now I am standing at number two
And you are at number three

And Jill lets Billy in front of her
Why? I'm not quite sure
But now I'm only number three
And you are number four

Then Billy lets Mike, Jack and Toby in
'Cos Billy is their best mate
And now I'm seventh in the queue
And you are at number eight

By the time the dinner lady
Comes to open the canteen door
I'm at number twenty-three
And you're at twenty-four

Then the dinner lady calls you to the front
Because you were the gold star winner
I was first out of the classroom
But I'm last in the line for dinner

Rhyming Couplets

We call lines that rhyme in pairs **rhyming couplets** (because, of course, they are a couple of lines that rhyme). When you read rhyming couplets out loud you often find they have a sing-song effect, which is why they are often used for funny poems. In *Forming a Band* the lines rhyme *okay* **(a)** / *play* **(a)**, *hop* **(b)** / *pop* (b), *soul* **(c)** / *roll* **(c)** and so on. So we say rhyming couplets rhyme **a a b b c c**.

Forming a Band

I said, Let's form a band, okay?
My mate said, Great – what shall we play?
How about Punk? Boogie-woogie? Hip-hop?
Acid-soul-house-jazz or Pop?
60s, Flower-power, Disco, Soul?
70s influenced? Plain Rock and Roll?
Ambient-psycho-techno-thrash?
Heavy metal? Hard core? Slash?
80s, Romantics, Garage... Shed?

Said I, Let's play with my skateboard instead.

Interlaced Rhymes

In the first poem I rhymed the second line of each verse with the fourth. It's a very common and quiet way to rhyme – not drawing attention to itself, letting the meaning of the poem stand out, but helping the sound and flow of the poem gently along. Slightly more complicated are **interlaced rhymes** where the first and third lines also rhyme (**a b a b**).

The Head Teacher's Dilemma

The remote won't control the TV
I think that the battery's gone
There's a disk stuck in the DVD
The computer won't turn on

The microwave won't behave. It keeps pinging!
The hot water just won't warm
The school alarms refuse to stop ringing
Because of last night's storm

The weeds keep growing, the field needs mowing
(I can't find the running track)
My office bin is overflowing
The answer phone answers me back

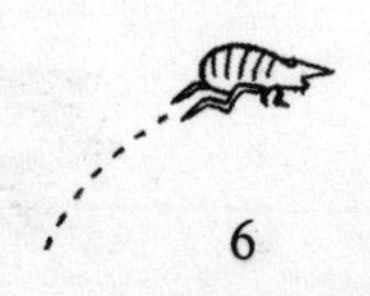

Billy's dropped his plastic crane
And it's blocking up the loo
There are parked cars jamming up the lane
'Cos the school gates won't undo

I can't lock up, can't turn out the light
I'm going to get the sack
I'm going to have to stay the night
I'll be glad when the caretaker's back

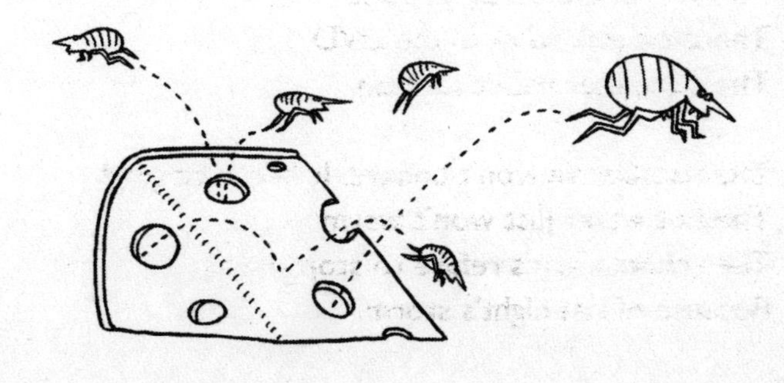

Here are some more poems using these three rhyming schemes (**a b c b** rhymes, interlaced rhymes and rhyming couplets). Can you see which is which?

Astrologically Speaking

I was born under the sign of the footballer
My birth colour Chelsea Blue
My rising moon is The Goalkeeper
The formation of stars 4 – 4 – 2

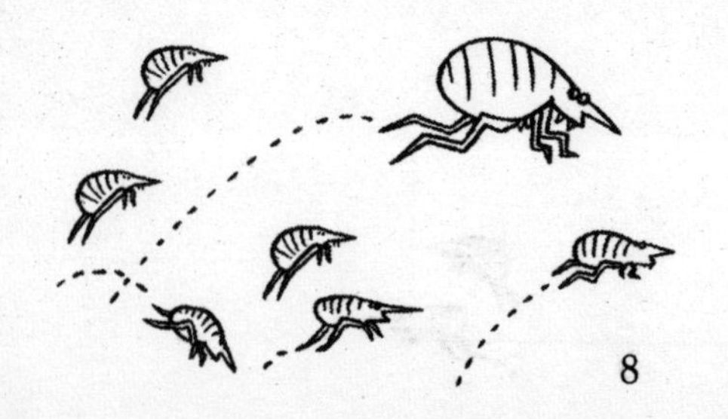

Family Hobbies

Brother Bart?
Likes art
Sister Hayley?
Ukulele
Dad?
Football mad
Mum?
A rugby scrum
Auntie Rose?
Sewing clothes
Uncle Sly?
DIY
Gramps?
Collecting stamps
Gran?
Baking a flan
Great-grandad Marcel?
Miming
And my hobby is...?

Giving

Ed gave me his birthday badge
I gave Ed my moon rock
Ed gave me his juicy peach
I gave Ed my left sock

Ed gave me his hamsters
Jimmy, Digs and Jack
Mum found them in my bedroom
And I had to give them back

Mum made Ed give my sock back
So I returned his peach
And Ed returned my moon rock
(I'd found it on the beach)

I returned Ed's birthday badge
And Mum said, Good. That's that.
She went downstairs to the kitchen
And I gave Ed our cat

No Show

I'm sorry I didn't turn up for the game
But the cat climbed into the tumble drier
I'm sorry we lost – but I'm not to blame.
I sat on a match and my trousers caught fire

I'm sorry they scored again and again
And I am the goalie, but what could I do?
I was leaving the house – it started to rain –
And the dog needed painting bright blue

So, we're out of the Cup. I'd have come if I could
But an alien came down and kidnapped my brother
You may think these excuses are not very good
But any excuse is as good as another

Ten Things to Do with Old Lottery Tickets

Make a tiny carrier bag
Stick to a pencil and use as a flag
Roll into a tooth-pick
Mop up mouse sick
Make an origami Yeti
Cut to small bits for confetti
Make into a paper aeroplane
Use to cover up an ice-cream stain
Paint gold to decorate the Christmas tree
But if the ticket's a winner – give it to me!

You might think that making a long or complicated word rhyme with another would add a serious note to a poem. But it usually makes it more comical. Maybe this is because when short words rhyme they don't attract too much attention. The same goes for rhyming unusual words. It might be fun to write a poem rhyming *enchilada*, the *Spanish Armada* and the *capital of Nevada*.

Hare and the Tortoise

When the hare raced the tortoise and the tortoise won
The hare was very dejected
The tortoise was driving a Porsche 911
So the outcome was not unexpected

Other Rhyme Schemes

There are lots of variations on these rhymes of course. Otherwise poetry would get boring very quickly. For example, sometimes poets rhyme three lines together (**a a a**). This is called a **tercet**.

Sometimes poets like to mix the way lines rhyme and take you by surprise!

My Goat

I've a goat called Pete
And he likes to eat

Carrots and peas
Potatoes and cheese
He chews the breeze

Worms and snails
Bags of nails
Whales' tails

Skipping ropes
Scented soaps
Microscopes

Bars of Snickers
Football stickers
Granny's knickers

He eats so much, I have
a question
Why does he not get
indigestion?

Lost Souls

Lost souls that wander
Lost souls that fly
Through the cold and careless
Moonlit sky
Searching for who knows what
Or why

Comets falling
Owls in flight
A broken promise
A family fight
Vampires hiding
From the light

From the window
On this run-down estate
I pass the time, I dream
I wait
Lost souls can surely
Glimpse our fate

Maybe I'll join you
Fly high like a lark
Blazing for seconds
A soaring spark
One moment of dazzle
In the forever of dark

The **monorhyme** uses only one rhyme sound. The master of using one continuous rhyme, but keeping the meaning spot on, is Nick Toczek.

Here, as well as the single rhyme, he repeats the word *you*, which adds to the rhythm, and the fun.

In Bed

Nick Toczek

That noise on the stair you
just heard, did it scare you?
I thought so. I swear you
are shivering where you
are curled up right there. You
can't look. You don't dare. You
fear for your welfare. You
hear breathing, aware you
have us here. Beware! You
quite rightly despair. You
see we're here to share you,
to rip you and tear you,
you'll be past repair. You
should say one last prayer. You
see we're your nightmare. You
will scream. We won't care. You
are doomed. We won't spare you.

I had fun with the rhymes in this next poem. It uses monorhyme – but I realised that if you add the word *fish* to almost any object you can think of, you end up with a word that does actually sound like a real (although sometimes very odd) fish.

This and That Fish

A catfish
Looks a bit like a cat
A hatfish
Looks like a cowboy hat
A batfish
Hangs from a cave like a bat
A chatfish
Often pops round for a chat
With the flatfish
Who lives in the ground-floor flat
With the gnatfish
Who zizzes around like a gnat
And a that fish
(I think that I'll finish this poem
like that)

(But first I'll take the dogfish
out for a swim)

Repetition (saying the same thing more than once) is used a lot in poetry. Sometimes it helps drive the poem along, emphasising the rhythm. Sometimes it is used to split a poem into sections or verses. Or it's used as a chorus – as you would in a song. In this poem the repeated words 'Who goes home?', together with the monorhyme, imitate a beating drum. This is a powerful poem. Read it out loud for the full effect!

Who Goes Home?

GK Chesterton

In the city set upon slime and loam,
They cry in their Parliament, "Who goes home?"
And there comes no answer in arch or dome,
For none in the city of graves goes home.
Yet these shall perish and understand,
For God has pity on this great land.
Men that are men again: Who goes home?
Tocsin and trumpeter! Who goes home?
For there's blood on the grass and blood on the foam,
And blood on the body, when Man comes home.
And a voice valedictory: Who is for victory?
Who is for liberty?
Who goes home?

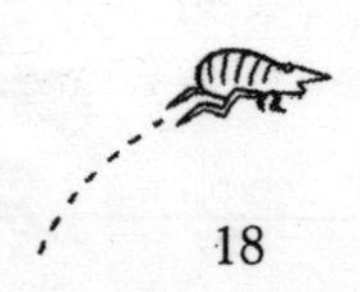

Other Kinds of Rhymes

Rhymes at the Beginning (Alliteration)

If we begin some of the words in our poem with the same sound, it's called **alliteration**. Alliteration is a form of rhyme – but it happens at the beginnings of words rather than at their ends.

A B Poem

If I could Be any Beast in Britain
I'd Be something Beginning with B
Like a Butterfly, Bug or a Beetle
And I'd Buzz about quite happily

Because B is a Brilliant letter
It's better than O, P or Q
If I could I'd Be a Bumble Bee
'Cos a B is much Better than U.

A Brandt's Bat, a Brown rat or Badger
Or a Bird on the wing or a nest
Like a Bittern or Blackbird or Buzzard
Yes, Beginning with B is the Best

If I could Be any Beast in Britain
I'd Be something Beginning with B
A Butterfly, Bug or a Beetle
Then wouldn't you want to Be me?

The You Can Be ABC

You can be
an artistic actor or a brainy barrister
a clever conductor or a dynamic dancer
an evil enemy or a fantastic friend
a green-fingered gardener or a healing herbalist
an interesting inventor or a jovial jolly juggler
a keen kitchen designer or a loggerheaded
lumberjack
a melodious musician or a neat newsreader
an over-the-top opera singer or a princely-paid
pop star
a quipping quiz master or a rich rugby player
a serious scientist or a typewriting traveller
an uppity umpire or a vigorous vet
a wonderful winner or an expert xylophonist
a yelling yachtsperson or a zealous zoologist.
So go to it, you can do it.
Someone's got to, why not you?
And who is going to stop you?
The only person who can stop you –
that's YOU!

Many poems are based on the alphabet, like the last one in which I used the ABC to get my 'You Can Be' message across. But this is my favourite alphabet poem.

The Lazy Poet's Alphabet

Gerard Benson

A is for Ankle and Auntie and Air
B is for Bottom and Button and Bear
C is for Clock which is worked by a Cog
D is for Dalmatian a nice spotty Dog
E is for Everything Else

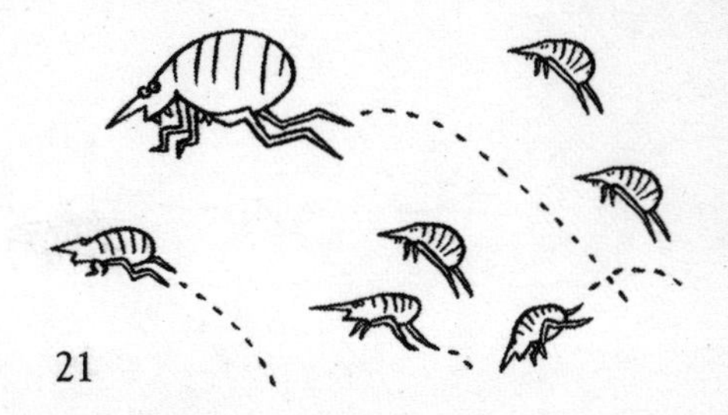

Rhymes in the Middle
(Consonance and Assonance)

So, now we know we can make the ends and the beginnings of words rhyme, but there's lots more we can do, too. For example we can rhyme the vowel sounds in the middle of words (this is called **assonance**) – as in the 'ee' sound of *sneeze*, *tweet*, *weave* and *meal*. Or we can rhyme the consonants in the middle of the words (this is called **consonance**). This has a similar effect to alliteration but the rhymes occur in the middle of the words – such as the B sounds in *rabbit*, *table*, *baby* and *robber*.

These rhymes aren't usually found at the ends of lines like regular rhymes – but are used to aid the poem's rhythm or maybe to enhance the mood, as in *Garden Shed*. In the first verse, for example, I've used repetition (*spider*, *spider*), alliteration (*mildew* and *mouldy*), assonance (*spider* and *ivy*) and assonance and consonance together (*broken* and *choking*.)

The important thing to remember though is that these techniques should not look too obvious. It's fun sometimes to analyse a poem, to see how the poet wrote it – but it's much more important, I think, to read it purely for enjoyment's sake!

When you read the poem – read it out loud.

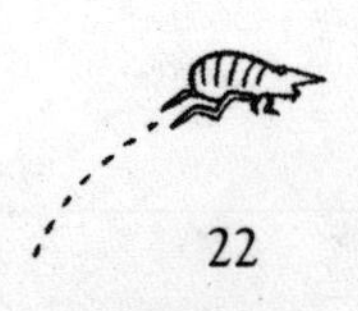

Garden Shed

Spider, spider
Broken, choking
Mildew, mouldy
Ivy creeping

Spider, spider
Cobwebs, dead bugs
Hedgehog sleeping
Sagging shelving

Spider, spider
Grimy, slimy
Snails and slugs
Jagged, slipping

Spider, spider
Hiding, lurking
Damp and cramped
An anxious feeling

Spider, spider
Oozing, seeping
Broken jam jars
Fertilizer

Used screws, fuses
Glues and nails
Rusty, musty
Stale and fungi

Old boot, darkness
Something hiding
Darkness, scratching
Spider, spider

At first glance, many of the lines in this poem do not appear to rhyme. But look carefully, and remember the different ways of rhyming, or, even better, read it out loud…

How to Find Our House

Head south until you reach the end of land
Take off your shoes and socks
Walk on to the beach
And down to the ocean
Across the sand and rocks

Listen to the whoosh of surf
The suck of shingle
The sea's wet kiss
Turn left
And head for those distant cliffs
In the mist

You'll pass the tangle of orange-glow netting
Snagged with pebbles and shells
Pass the bleached beached driftwood
And the rotting crab smells
Pass the broken plastic chair
Thrown back by the waves
Pass the black, cracked truck mudguard
And the message on the sand
Jesus Saves

When you reach the Martello Tower
Turn left, with your back to the sea
And in the window of that white cottage
The one on the left
There's me
Writing this poem
And waving.
You're just in time for tea

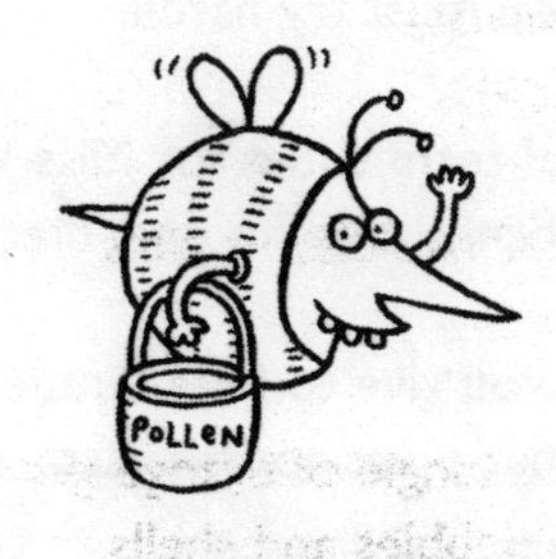

Half Rhymes

In a **half rhyme**, the first part of the words rhyme but the following syllable or syllables don't. As though the poet wants to rhyme but suddenly changes his or her mind. They work like whole rhymes – but slow the poem down. This could be because your brain is expecting the second word to rhyme properly and when it doesn't, it stops for a moment to try and work out why.

After the Summer

Like the picture you show Miss Card
Who says, You must try harder

Or the end-of-term chocs for Miss Wiley
Who says, Thanks, but I'm on a diet

Or the scarf you give to Miss Draper
Who says, That's just not my taste, dear

Or the day that you hoped wouldn't come
Back to school after the summer

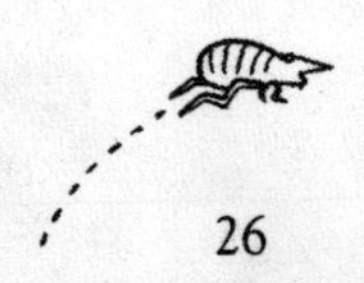

Internal Rhymes

As we've seen, rhymes can come anywhere in a poem, not just at the end of lines. Regular rhymes that appear in the middle of lines are called **internal rhymes**. They are often used to accentuate the rhythm of a poem.

The tarantella is a fast Italian dance – and so it's no surprise to find lots of internal rhymes in the poem *Tarantella*, giving it a very rhythmic sound. Read it out loud to catch the rhythm. You'll also spot lots of alliteration, assonance, consonance and end rhymes. The first verse is great fun (I love the rhymes *Miranda* and *veranda*, and *fleas* and *Pyrenees*) but the second verse gets more serious.

When you read it, listen to how the rhymes and rhythm work with the meaning of the words. You can hear a dance when you read:

the girl gone chancing,
Glancing,
Dancing,
Backing and advancing

Then in the second verse, listen for the heavy, hopeless, monotonous thud of the walking dead:

No sound
In the walls of the halls where falls
The tread
Of the feet of the dead to the ground

Tarantella

Hilaire Belloc

Do you remember an Inn,
Miranda?
Do you remember an Inn?
And the tedding and the spreading
Of the straw for a bedding,
And the fleas that tease in the High Pyrenees,
And the wine that tasted of tar?
And the cheers and the jeers of the young muleteers
(Under the vine of the dark veranda)?
Do you remember an Inn, Miranda,
Do you remember an Inn?
And the cheers and the jeers of the young muleteers
Who hadn't got a penny,
And who weren't paying any,
And the hammer at the doors and the din?
And the hip! hop! hap!
Of the clap
Of the hands to the swirl and the twirl
Of the girl gone chancing,
Glancing,
Dancing,
Backing and advancing,
Snapping of the clapper to the spin
Out and in--
And the ting, tong, tang of the guitar!

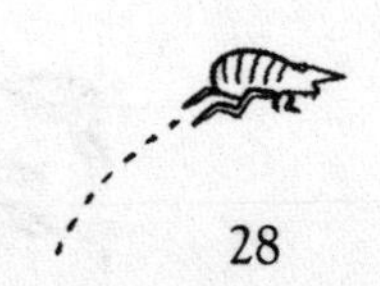

Do you remember an Inn,
Miranda?
Do you remember an Inn?

Never more;
Miranda,
Never more.
Only the high peaks hoar;
And Aragon a torrent at the door.
No sound
In the walls of the halls where falls
The tread
Of the feet of the dead to the ground,
No sound:
But the boom
Of the far waterfall like doom.

Some Kinds of Poems

There are lots of different forms of poetry. And most of them have their own special rhyming scheme. Let's start with a very short one.

Clerihews

This four-line celebrity poem was invented by Edmund Clerihew Bentley. The first line introduces the famous person that the poem's all about. The lines can be any length – but they must rhyme in couplets (**a a b b**).

Sir Christopher Wren

E. Clerihew Bentley

Said Sir Christopher Wren,
"I'm having lunch with some men.
If anyone calls,
Say I'm designing Saint Paul's."

Daniel Defoe

E. Clerihew Bentley

Daniel Defoe
Lived a long time ago
He had nothing to do so
He wrote Robinson Crusoe

Michael Owen*

Michael Owen, Michael Owen
Runs so fast his pants are showing
Kicks the ball for all his worth
Now it's orbiting the Earth

* I wrote this when Michael Owen was Liverpool Football Club's best striker. (And he scored loads of goals for England too.)

Shoe the Blues Away

King Tut
Was a nut
When he had the blues
He bought a new pair of shoes

Limericks

Almost everyone's familiar with limericks: they have been around for hundreds of years. They have five lines (two long, two short, one long) that rhyme **a a b b a** and a regular rhythm – read a few out loud and you'll quickly get the hang of it! There was a huge craze for limericks in Victorian times. They were made popular by Edward Lear – who *I* think used to cheat a bit by repeating the first line at the end. They're fun to write, but tricky customers. By the way, because of their sing-song rhythm it's almost impossible to write a serious limerick. There's a challenge for you.

The Old Person of Buda*

Edward Lear

There was an Old Person of Buda
Whose conduct grew ruder and ruder
Till at last, with a hammer
They silenced his clamour
By smashing that Person of Buda

* Edward Lear was very good at making up nonsense words and funny names, but Buda is a real place (it's half of Budapest, in Hungary).

There was an Old Man of Coblenz

Edward Lear

There was an Old Man of Coblenz
The length of whose legs was immense
He went with one prance
From Turkey to France
That surprising Old Man of Coblenz

There was an Old Man of the Coast

Edward Lear

There was an Old Man of the coast
Who placidly sat on a post
But when it was cold
He relinquished his hold
And called for some hot buttered toast

Never Pick a Fight with a Fairy

Never pick a fight with a fairy
She may seem insubstantial and airy
But her magic is such
That with just one light touch
She could turn you to jelly. That's scary.

Roald Dahl

Roald Dahl – where is your N?
At birth, did a slip of the pen
Help your name achieve fame
It would not be the same
If you were called Ronald. (Or Sven)*

*or Tarka

The Young Poet Called Brice

There was a young poet called Brice
Who never wrote one word when ten would suffice
His limericks in particular had lines that went on and on with far too many words to the point of being ridiculous
But his rhymes were meticulous
That verbose young poet called Brice

And finally, on the subject of limericks and Edward Lear's made-up words…

Items in the Edward Lear Museum

Thirty-nine bottles of Ring Bo Ree
A sieve that has travelled the Western Sea
And in pride of place
A crumbobblious case,
And a branch from the old Bong Tree

A runcible spoon, a silvery bee
A zebra from far away Jellibolee
Some waterproof clothes
A beard and the nose
Of a Quangle Wangle Quee

Ballads
(Poems that Tell Stories)

Ballads were tales told by wandering troubadours, or storytellers, in the Middle Ages. They were often written in rhyme (which really makes them poems) to make them easy to remember. They would often have a chorus for people to join in and the language was usually kept simple, as the storyteller's audiences would very often be uneducated. Ballads have four lines and a regular rhythm. The first and third lines have four beats and the second and fourth lines have three. They usually rhyme **a b c b** (the one below also uses **a b a b**). Pop ballads and pop songs still use this style today.

Why the Bat Flies at Night

Once, when the moon was as bright as the sun
And the stars lit up the sky
And the day and the night were both as one,
The bat came flying by

The bat flew by fast and furious
And attached to his back with string
Was a basket. The animals were curious
They said, Bat, what is in that thing?

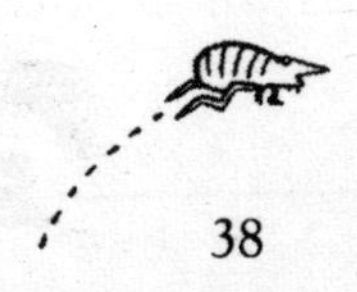

Ah, said the bat, well, this afternoon
I was given a task to do
To take this basket up to the moon
But what's in it? I haven't a clue.

But the bat was no long-distance flyer
And he had to lie down for a sleep
So, due to the others' insistence,
The lion opened the basket to peep

Then all at once from the basket
There came a most terrible sight
A shadow that fell like a dark net
Bringing the blackness of night

And that is why bats rise at twilight
And they sleep through the bright hours of day
Why they chivvy and chase the dark slivers of night
The darkness they let get away

Tongue Twisters

Tongue twisters use every rhyming device, especially alliteration – the whole point is that the poem is difficult to say out loud. They are very hard to write (although there's a good method on page 78) because they not only have to be difficult to say, they also have to make sense! Even more importantly, tongue twisters should be fun.

Here are a couple of traditional favourites of mine to get us started. Don't forget, you really need to read them out loud (and fast) for best effect... good luck with that!

Night Light

Anon

You've no need to light a night-light
On a light night like tonight,
For a night-light's light's a slight light,
And tonight's a night that's light.
When a night's light, like tonight's light,
It is really not quite right
To light night-lights with their slight lights
On a light night like tonight.

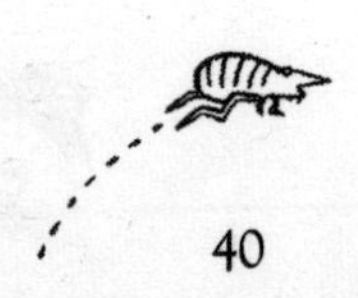

The Tree Toad

Anon

A tree toad loved a she-toad
Who lived up in a tree
He was a two-toed tree toad
But a three-toed toad was she.
The two-toed tree toad tried to win
The three-toed she-toad's heart
For the two-toed tree toad loved the ground
That the three-toed tree toad trod.
But the two-toed tree toad tried in vain.
He couldn't please her whim.
From her tree toad bower
With her three-toed power
The she-toad vetoed him.

The Unwed Shropshire Shepherdess

Nick Toczek

She said to Shaun she sought some short-shorn sheep.
"What sorts of short-shorn sheep?" said Shaun.
She'd seemed to Shaun unsure what sorts of short-shorn sheep she sought.

Shaun sought to sort what sorts of short-shorn sheep she sought.
Shaun's Shropshire shop sold six sorts of short-shorn sheep.
So she was shown Shaun's shop's six short-shorn sheep sorts.

She said she was sure she'd seen some short-shorn sorts of sheep she sought.
She said she'd sort the sorts she sought and see Shaun soon. "Sure," said Shaun.
She smiled, sure Shaun was the short-shorn Shropshire sort she so sought.

Haikus and Senryus

A **haiku** or **senryu** is a Japanese form of short poem, usually written in three lines with five, seven and five syllables to each line. In Japanese poetry, haikus are usually about the natural world, while senryus are about the human world. Senryus are often comical. Haiku and senryu poems don't usually rhyme, but here are some senryus that do.

Spot the Fairy Tales (Five Little Senryus)

James Carter

1

Little voice calling
an urgent word of warning
"The sky is falling!"

2

So no porky pies:
plenty of huffs and puffs... plus
a hot bot to boot!

3

"Hey babe, way up there –
I've found neither lift nor stair –
please let down your hair!"

4

"My cunning plannie –
If I can't nab that Hoodie,
I'll grab her Grannie!"

5

She's poshed up in bling.
Grooving with the future king.
Slipper fits. Kerching!!!!!

Sonnets

The sonnet is a very old form of verse that came to England nearly 500 years ago, from Italy. The English version was made famous by William Shakespeare, and his sonnets are probably the most famous in the whole of English literature.

There are fourteen lines in a sonnet. There are several different ways to rhyme them but one of the most popular ways in English is the one Shakespeare used:

a b a b
c d c d
e f e f
g g

Complicated, eh? Sonnets are usually written in "iambic pentameter", which means each line has five pairs of syllables ('pent' means 'five', as in pentagon). 'Iambic' means that each pair of syllables has one unstressed syllable and one stressed one. So each line goes di **dah** di **dah** di **dah** di **dah** di **dah**, like the line below. (Say it out loud and you'll hear yourself put more stress on the words in bold!)

If **you** would **put** the **key** in**side** the **lock**

Sprint

The air is hot. The sky is blue. Expect
No favours from the sun. You stand alone
Survey the stadium, the crowd. Inspect
The track. A moment's doubt. Can it be done?

And then the training, days, months, years – kicks in
And you are focused on the prize. You know
With certainty what you must do. Begin
With deep breaths. Stretch. Relax. It's time to go.

A billion eyes are watching. You can't hide.
There's silence. You can hear your beating heart.
You crouch. Into the starting blocks you slide.
You wait. Time stops. You hope there's no false start.

Marks. Get set. Kick. Ten seconds and you're done.
You are the bullet in the starter's gun.

As well as writing plays William Shakespeare wrote lots of sonnets. If you're interested you might like to seek them out.

Kennings

Kennings originally come from Scandinavia. These poems use two words, often hyphenated or compound words, to describe a more straightforward word, but in a poetic way. This kenning uses lots of assonance, consonance and alliteration.

Mum & Dad

Tenderskin & Roughchin
Dawngreeter & Toastjuggler
Cuddlebear & Grizzlybear
Firmhand & Strongarm
Sadsmile & Grinner
Busybee & Grasshopper
Spicegrinder & Potstirrer
Sunsoaker & Ballspinner
Spidershrieker & Jarcatcher
Taleteller & Dreamweaver
Earthmother & Earthmover

A Mixed Bag

And finally in this part of the book, a selection of all sorts of rhymes. See if you can work out which sort of rhyme each one is.

James Bond's Car

So this, you say, was James Bond's car
Did you get it from a dealer?
I love the feel of the steering wheel.
Don't touch that lever!

I love the colour – the go-faster stripes
The upholstery of leather
And the nozzle for making oil skids.
Don't touch that lever!

An in-board computer with gadgets galore
Pours lemonade – if you need a breather –
And is this a rocket launcher? Wow!
Don't touch that lever!

I wish I had a James Bond car.
It's a real scene-stealer.
And look – it's got ejector seats.
Don't touch that...
AAAaaaaaaaaaaaaaaaaaaaahhhhhhhhh

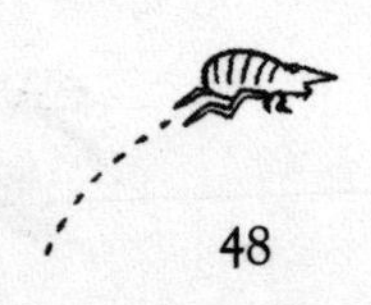

Joan of Arc

Everyone thought it odd
that Joan of Arc heard voices

From God.

For being a witch and for foretelling that the
English would be defeated by the French and
thrown out of France (except for Calais)
she was burned at the stake which,
in those less-civilised and deadly times,
is about what one might expect.

But as it turned out she was
Correct.

Making a Poem

If you say
something
and make it rhyme
that's
not
necessarily
a poem,
okay?

But
a kiss
always
is

Mr Walton's On The Playground

Michael's ball is on the roof
And Darren wants a fight
Little Kelly Kupcake
Is dangling from her kite

But Mr Walton's on the playground
So everything will be all right

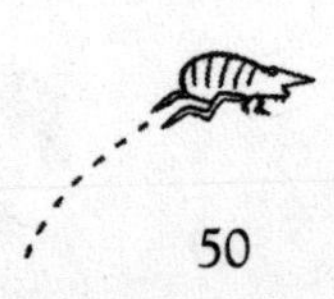

Noel went in the girl's loo
And gave the girls a fright
Yaseen won't let Gemma kiss him
But Derek Trubsall might

But Mr Walton's on the playground
So everything will be all right

Randeep's lost his pet rat
(He says it doesn't bite)
Michael says – Aren't people small
When viewed from this great height?

But Mr Walton's on the playground
So everything will be all right

Tommy's foot is swelling up
His laces are too tight
Now Michael's stuck up on the roof.
He'll have to stay all night

But Mr Walton's on the playground
So everything will be er...

Where's Mr Walton gone?

Goal Defender

Ball plucker
Ball catcher
Ball puncher
Muddy scrambler
Fast diver
Crowd sorter
Long kicker
Expert thrower
Ace defender
Time passer
Wall-builder
Penalty saver
Game winner

A Cautionary Tale

Don't climb on roofs
Pop told young Drew
For one day you
Will fall straight through

But Drew ignored
The words of Pop
And climbed the roof
To the very top

Alas, Pop's warning
Did come true
The roof gave way
And Drew fell through

But Drew had made
A lucky call
For Pop was there
To break his fall

Moral

If your kids ignore
The things you say
And climb on roofs
Keep out the way!

Holiday Treasures

A dull white pebble
That misses the ocean
A Greek postage stamp
Of Aristotle's head
A strand of dried seaweed
Out of its depth
A fragile ball of sponge
Found on the seabed
A postcard of ruins
With a sizzling blue sky
A photograph of Grandad
With the dog with one eye

My Dad

My Dad's a cobbler.
He mends shoes.
He's my cobbling Dad.

He dropped the hammer on his toe.
He's my hobbling, cobbling Dad.

Dad had an argument with a customer.
He's my squabbling, hobbling, cobbling Dad.

So he made her a raspberry jelly.
He's my wobbling, squabbling, hobbling, cobbling Dad.

Then he ate it all himself.
He's my gobbling, wobbling, squabbling, hobbling, cobbling Dad.

Mum and Dad's Bedroom

When my friends come round to stay
I try to keep them well away:
My Mum and Dad's bedroom's not cool –
The opposite in fact, it's full of...

Drippy candles, hippy sandals
Piles of boots and baggy suits
Motorbike bits, inclined to rust
Piles of books with inch-thick dust
Earrings, brooches, incense holder
A plaster cast of Noddy Holder
A dog basket behind the door
(Our dog died in ninety-four)
Perfume bottles obscure the mirror
Mugs with mould and last week's dinner
Varnished poppy heads with seeds
Silver chains and strings of beads
Scarves and headbands, capes and cloaks
Tee shirts sporting silly jokes
Posters, leaflets, pots, a kite
A faded flag wrapped round the light
China pigs and elephants
Smelly socks and bras and pants
Some broken dolls, the head of Ted
And hiding somewhere there's a bed

Thank You Note

Thank you for having me, Auntie Sue
I had a wonderful time with you
I'm sorry I dropped your specs down the loo
And I'm sorry about the superglue, too
When Uncle Dick fell asleep in the chair
And I glued bits of string to his bald head for hair
And I'm sorry the budgie escaped, that's the truth
And Uncle Dick chased it – and fell off the roof
And he broke his good leg and knocked out a tooth
So thanks for the visit. I'll never forget it
And I'm sorry the cat caught the budgie and ate it

Missing Monty

Winter was coming
When Monty went missing
Oh, how I missed
His sibilant hissing

I searched high and low
I searched thin and long
Oh, where had my
Pet python gone?

Soon Christmas carols
Then Auld Lang Syne
Of missing Monty
There was no sign

Then just when I'd given him
Up for dead
On the first day of Spring
He turned up in my bed

Safe in my mattress
Tucked away out of sight
Just think, I'd been keeping
Him warm every night

Alien Nursery Rhyme

You should definitely read this one out loud.

Yak enjilwen
Tuppa hil toof
Etcha payler
Walter

Yak feltoonen
Bro ciskrownen
Yilkaim
Tumplingaf tuh

Oopyak kotton ohm
Dittrota
Svasttas eegud
Kay porr

Ewent oobeh tu
Mendis edwiv
Finni gah han
Brough wenp aipah

Hill Adventure

The moon doth shine as bright as in the day
I sit upon the see-saw wondering why
she left me. Boys and girls come out to play.
But I'm bereft. I think I'm going to cry.
I gave her chocolate and I praised her skill
At skateboarding and football not to mention
Arm wrestling. As we slowly climbed the hill
To fetch some water, did I sense a tension?
She seemed pre-occupied. She hardly spoke
And as we turned the handle to the well
I asked her, Jill, please tell me it's a joke.
She said, I've found another bloke. I fell,
I spun, head over heels into the dark
Down to the bottom where I broke my heart

When Words Don't Rhyme

Some words are impossible to rhyme. I always thought that there wasn't a rhyme for *orange* until I saw an estate agent's office in Lewes, near Brighton. The agent was called Roland Gorringe. So I wrote this poem. (The last line doesn't quite rhyme. But it's very close!)

The Poet Called Gorringe

There was a young poet called Gorringe
Who was after a rhyme-word for orange
With a tinge of regret
Said, I've not found one yet
As he sucked on a peppermint lozenge

There are lots of words that are tricky to rhyme. *Purple*, *silver*, *galaxy*, *chocolate*, *monster*... can you think of any more?

Poets get around this in lots of ways. The easiest is to move the word you want to rhyme so that it's not at the end of the line any more. But you can use a close rhyme, or use two words (as in *door hinge* for *orange*).

Or you can make a word up! If you look *murple* up on your computer you'll find lots of definitions for it – including "a word for a word that has no rhyme". But none of the definitions have made their way into the official dictionary yet.

I wrote this for James Carter's book of the same name – but in the end he didn't use it.

How to Turn Your Teacher Purple*

In Cookery
Me and Dean
Made some tea
That turned our teacher green

In Chemistry
Me and Drew
Made some dye
That turned our teacher blue

In Biology
Me and Fred
Embarrassed our teacher
And turned her red

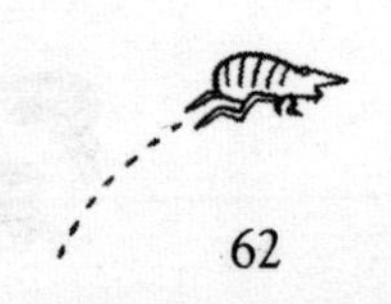

In Geography
We visited Storringe
We sat in the sun
And our teacher turned orange

On a trip to the Dungeons
We turned out the light
The class went BOO!
And our teacher turned white

In Science
Me and Tim Wilver
Created a pill
That turned our teacher silver

In the Art Room
Me and Jane Murple
Knocked over the paint
And turned our teacher purple

* Okay, okay. I admit it. I cheated by making a few of the names up.

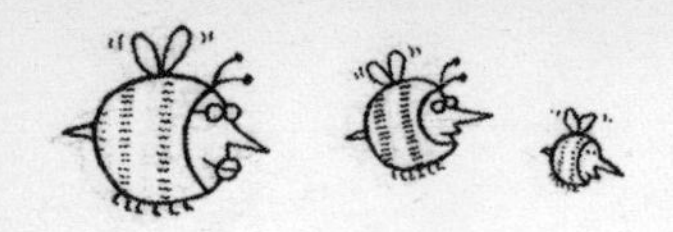

Part 2: How to write Rhyming Poems

1 Poems are Fun

Welcome to Part Two. This section of the book is for budding poets. If you enjoy writing poems you'll find lots of useful tips and ideas here.

If you've never written a poem before but would like to (or if you've never even thought of writing one and actually think you can't and are nervous of trying) just have a go at one of the examples here.

Anyone – including you – can write a poem by following a few simple steps. Of course, not everyone can write a brilliant, amazing, jaw-dropping, laugh-out-loud masterpiece. To write well takes time and, like everything else, whether it's football, table-tennis, painting the Mona Lisa or learning the guitar, lots and lots of practice.

Although this book is about rhyme, do remember rhythm, too. The beat of a poem is probably the most important thing to get right. When you've written your first draft, read your poem out loud – to yourself or someone else. And if it doesn't sound smooth and have a flowing rhythm, alter it. Never be afraid to change the words around to make a poem sound right.

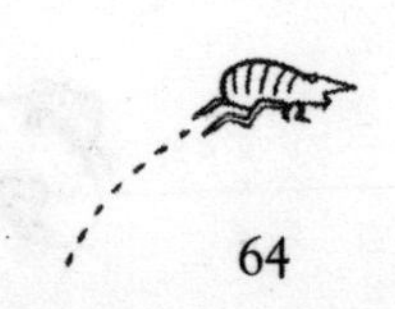

If you'd like to be a bit more serious about writing poems (or stories), why not do what professional writers do and get yourself a notebook? I carry my notebook with me absolutely everywhere I go because a good idea for a poem or a story can come to me at any time or any place: on the bus, walking to school, or in bed at two o'clock in the morning. And with my notebook on hand I can always jot the idea down and get back to it later when I have time to work on it.

Finally and most important of all – ENJOY POETRY! It can be fun exploring a poem. Sometimes I think it's like solving a puzzle, working out how the poet put the poem together, how the rhymes work and what the poem really means – especially when the meaning of a poem isn't really obvious. And creating a poem can sometimes be a bit like creating a puzzle.

But what I like best is simply to listen to or to read poems just for enjoyment's sake, like reading a good story or watching a film. When a poem catches you off guard and you find yourself guffawing or wiping away a tear – that's the best of all.

2 Starting from Scratch

If you suddenly find yourself having to write a poem for the first time – maybe for homework or just because the fancy takes you – here's a good way to get started.

Step One

Begin by making a list. Say, for example, you want to write a poem about winter. Give yourself a time limit of around about four minutes and write down as many words about winter as you can.

Think about the things associated with winter such as snow, Christmas, robins, icicles, rain, bare trees, and so on. Write down some wintry adjectives (describing words) such as cold, icy, chilly, dark, black, draughty. Write down some of the things you do in winter – Christmas shopping, making snowmen, playing football on muddy pitches, coming home from or going to school in the dark…

Write fast! You don't have to be neat and tidy. It's a list! And it doesn't matter if you write rubbish, because one idea leads to another, that's how our brains work. And sometimes something really stupid will remind you of something that would be great in a poem.

Remember, this isn't the poem, just a list of random information that will help you write it. And you need as much information as you can get together.

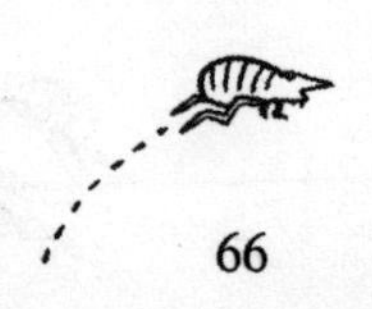

To recap:

1 Think of your subject.

2 Give yourself a time limit.

3 Write really fast. Be untidy if you have to be to get the words down.

4 Write down everything you think of, write single words, write about things you have done… let one word or phrase suggest others.

Step Two

Now look at what you've got on your list. Is there anything there that will make a poem?

A poem can be a list of words. (See page 75.) Or it can be a little story in poetic form. If I had chosen winter as my subject, I could tell about the time the snow on the porch roof fell on my dad's head, for example. Or it can be just a description of something.

For a haiku poem you only need seventeen syllables. Maybe there's one image that you could use from your list that would make a great haiku.

The following chapters will suggest some great ways to write a poem. Use your list and try them. And then attempt some other poems along the lines of those we've talked about in this book.

The important thing is just to have a go. You can't really fail. Remember, it's all part of learning the poet's skill – nobody expects you to write a masterpiece first time. But you might come up with something worth keeping. And there's no better feeling.

3 How To Find Rhymes

Here is a quick way to find a rhyme. Say you need a word to rhyme with *pin*. Simply write down the alphabet: A B C D E F G H I J… and so on. Then say out loud the end of the word (in this case *in*) with the sound of each letter of the alphabet, from A to Z. So you would say… a-in, b-in, c-in, d-in, e-in, f-in, g-in, h-in, i-in, j-in… and so on. In this example we already have found four words to rhyme with *pin* – *bin*, *din*, *fin* and *gin* – and there are a lot more as you go through the alphabet.

Once you've been through the alphabet, try adding in an R or an L as the second letter, because they are letters that often go with others at the beginning of words – you'll find *grin* in this case.

And don't forget to start your word with SH, CH and TH – now we've found *shin*, *chin* and *thin*.

We've got enough words already to help us write a poem that rhymes.

Some poets like to use rhyming dictionaries – a really good one is *Black's Rhyming and Spelling Dictionary* (A & C Black) by Pie Corbett and Ruth Thomson. I sometimes use one, but not often, as I enjoy searching for rhymes myself, so I only use a rhyming dictionary if I'm really stuck, or sometimes just for inspiration: looking at a huge long list of words that rhyme can often give you an idea for a poem.

Just for fun, to test out your own rhyming skills, see how many words you can think of that rhyme with *sneeze*. There are 52 in my rhyming dictionary. But if you can think of 30, I'd say that was an excellent result. (You can get some clues from the cover and the pictures in this book.)

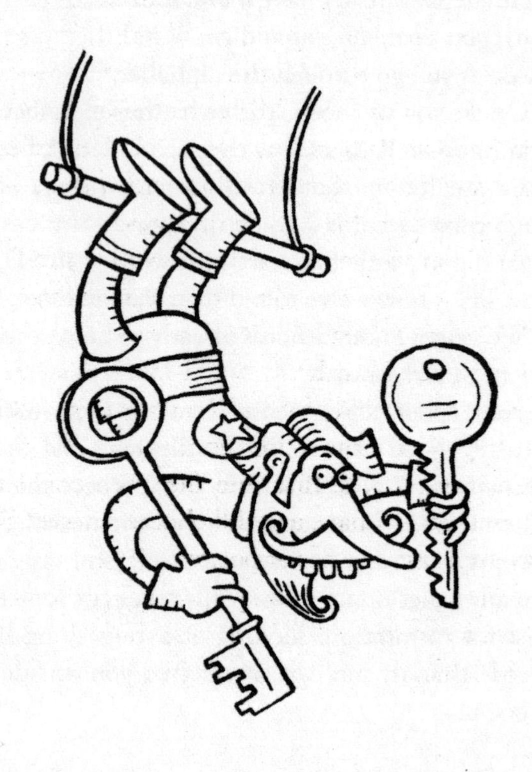

4 The Big Secret: last things first!

You may have noticed that the last line of a rhyming poem is often the most important. It's the one you remember as you finish reading. So if you're writing a rhyming poem, don't let that last line let you down.

It's sometimes easy to write three brilliant lines but then have real difficulty finding a rhyme that works well for the fourth line. And you should never use a word that doesn't really work. If you do you'll end up with a clunky poem, or one that makes no sense, or one that just sounds contrived – as if you've tried too hard to find a rhyme.

So I'll let you in on a secret – there is a trick that poets use. (And you can use this trick too.) They don't write the last line last.

Let's try this out by writing a four line verse. We want the last word of the second line to rhyme with the last word of the fourth line.

So think of the first line first. We could write about a pet – 'I have a ...' I'll choose *hamster*. So we have the first line of our poem:

I have a hamster

Now ignore the second line and move on to lines three and four. Think of things a hamster does – running in its wheel, eating, escaping from its cage. Use these for the poem. So we now have:

1) I have a hamster
2) (unwritten)
3) He runs in his wheel
4) And is always escaping from his cage

Now here's the trick! Think of a name to call your hamster – and rhyme it with the word cage. I'm going to call my hamster Sage. So now we have:

1) I have a hamster
2) His name is Sage
3) He runs in his wheel
4) And is always escaping from his cage

That's our basic verse. But like most first drafts, it still needs working on. We need to check that the rhythm of the poem is right. And we should see if anything else can be improved.

For a start, I'm going to change the hamster to a girl, as Sage is a more feminine name.

Then, if I read the poem out loud I can hear two beats (or stressed syllables) in each of the first three lines. I **have** a **ham**ster, her **name** is **Sage**, she **runs**

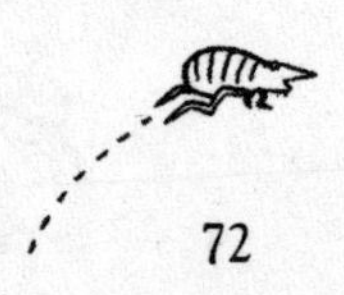

in her **wheel**...This gives the poem a rhythm. But the last line has four beats. So I need to shorten the last line to match the others.

I have a hamster
Her name is Sage
She runs in her wheel
And escapes from her cage

That sounds much better. Now I have a poem that rhymes naturally, makes sense and has a good rhythmic flow when read out loud. It tells a little story. But I wonder if I can improve it further. I think so.

The poem tells a story but it's a bit boring. Maybe she could escape from her cage in an unusual way. Maybe she's a super hamster and escapes by bending the bars of her cage? Or maybe she could just knock her wheel over...

I have a hamster
Her name is Sage
She knocked over her wheel
And escaped from her cage

But the important thing is, as I hope you can see from this example, that if we'd put 'cage' at the end of the second line and then finished the poem with

the hamster's name, Sage, the rhyme would have sounded and felt contrived.

I have a hamster
She escaped from her cage
She knocked over her wheel
Her name is Sage

By doing it back to front, we've created what reads like a clever rhyme.

So the trick is – always think of the last line first. And then find your rhyme.

5 List Poems

List poems don't have to rhyme, but it's fun when they do. And there's lots of opportunities for alliteration as well. Think of a subject. Animals work well (monkeys, dogs, tigers, owls, spiders) – as do items of clothing (shorts, pants, hats, shoes) or food (pizza, cheese, chocolate). Then give yourself a time limit – say three minutes – and write down as many adjectives to go with your subject as you can. Work really, really quickly. The more things you can think of the better. Then look at your list. You need to:

1. See if you can add a few more rhyming words.

2. Put everything into a good order. If you have words that rhyme, for example, put them together. Put the best words last. (As in The Big Secret – page 71.)

3. Don't be afraid to cross out anything you've written that's not very good. It's always better to write down more than you need and edit it out later. Most good writers do that.

4. Think up a little introduction and a way to end your poem. I've used some repetition in mine too.

Watch Out! There Are Monsters About

Watch out! There are monsters about
There are monsters about. Watch out!

There are rhyming monsters
Sliming monsters
Growling monsters
Scowling monsters
Frowning monsters
Drowning monsters
Boring monsters
Roaring monsters
Hairy monsters
Scary monsters

Watch out! There are monsters about
There are monsters about. Watch out!

Bad-egg-breath monsters
Scare-you-to-death monsters
Turn-you-to-stone monsters
Crunch-up-your-bone monsters
Kidnap-and-tie-you monsters
Breath-fire-and-fry-you monsters
Hiding-under-the-bed monsters
Biting-off-your-head monsters

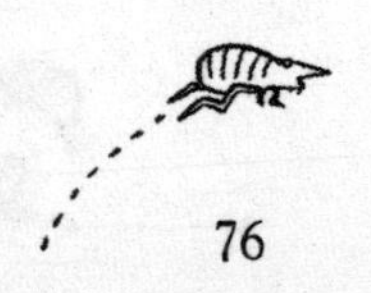

Lock your door. Run and hide
Warn everyone and shout
Watch out! There are monsters about
There are monsters about. Watch out!

6 How to Write a Tongue Twister

Tongue twisters are really difficult to write. First you have to find words that, when said one after the other quickly, become difficult to say. To do this you have to find rhyming words and use lots of alliteration. That's hard enough. But then the really tricky bit is ensuring that the poem makes sense. However – despair not! Here's an easy way of doing it.

Think of a subject for your poem. I shall use an animal. Let's think – something a bit unusual – but that starts with a good alliterative letter. S is always good for tongue twisters. Let's make our subject have a fairly easy rhyme, too. I'll go for SNAIL.

In the garden I found a snail

Now I'm going to keep adding adjectives that begin with an S sound And if possible a SN sound. As I add the the new word – the line will get longer. And hopefully more difficult to say out loud.

In the garden I found a snail
It was a sniffly snail
A smelly, sniffly snail

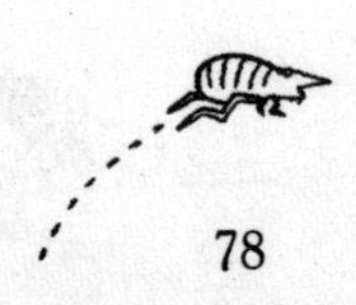

A silly, smelly, sniffly snail
A snacking, silly, smelly, sniffly, snail
A stupid, silly, smelly, sniffly, snail

And so on. You'll need to think of a good ending too.

And it got squashed on the street by a steamroller

You can experiment by adding words that rhyme.

In the garden I found a snail
It was a sniffly snail
It was a whiffy, sniffly, pale snail
It was a slippery, slimy, grimy, whiffy, sniffly pale snail

Finally read it out loud a few times. Listen to which words get in the way of other words and change things around until you're happy with the result.

7 Fun With Place Names

There's a terrific poem by Pie Corbett called *A Chance in France*. In it he finds things to do that rhyme with places all around the world. "Stay at home, Mum said, But I took a chance in France, Turned grey for the day in St Tropez, Forgot what I did in Madrid…" and so on. It's great fun.

So why not grab an atlas or book of maps and have a go yourself? In my version I've tried to think of games, names and places in Britain.

Playing Games with James in Staines

I played chess with Jess in Shoeburyness
And football with Paul in Donegal
Connect Four with Lenore on the shore of
 Loch More
Rummy with Mummy in Brumby
Monopoly with Polly in Hockley
Trivial Pursuit with Toots at Boots in Bootle
Whist with Fliss in Biss
Volleyball with Paul and Phil in Holleyhill
I played cards with Marge in Charde
Cricket with Lemony Snicket in Whitwick
Bridge with Midge in Ridge
Postman's knock with Jock by Lochwinnoch
Pitch and toss with Ross at King's Cross

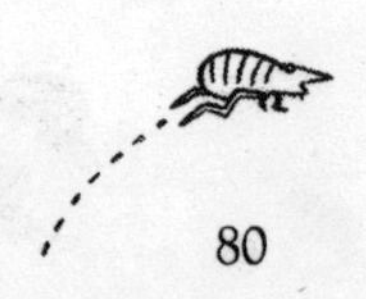

Musical chairs with Pam Ayres in Broadstairs
Boggle with Biggles in Diggle
Blind man's bluff with McDuff in Clough
And shove ha'penny with Benny in Abergavenny
Sardines with Dean and Jean in Bumbles Green
Badminton with Bea at Frinton-on-Sea
The ancient game of Go with Flo in Stow
Backgammon with Dan, Sam and Jan in Hameringham
And tic tac toe with Joe in Rotten Row

8 A Load of Nonsense

Lewis Carroll, like Edward Lear, was a great fan of nonsense. He wrote the fabulous *Alice's Adventures in Wonderland* and *Through the Looking-Glass*, both full of wonderful nonsense poems and parodies.

Here are the first two verses of his *The Mad Gardener's Song*:

He thought he saw an Elephant
That practised on a fife:
He looked again, and found it was
A letter from his wife.
'At length I realise,' he said,
'The bitterness of Life!'

He thought he saw a Buffalo
Upon the chimney-piece:
He looked again, and found it was
His Sister's Husband's Niece.
'Unless you leave this house,' he said,
'I'll send for the Police!'

Utter nonsense but very funny, made funnier, I think, by the great rhymes – *chimney-piece*, *niece* and *police*.

Nonsense poems are really good fun to write. Write down a few sensible lines first, based on everyday happenings: Getting up, having breakfast,

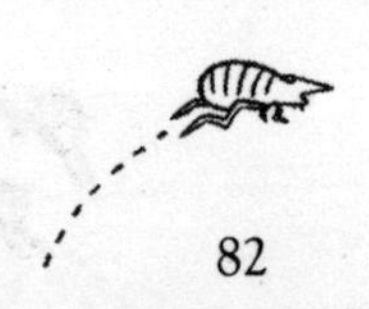

walking to school, running a race, playing netball or football. Anything you like.

Then start adding some ridiculous things. Change your cornflakes into worms and the breakfast table into an elephant or skateboard. Make the skate board jet-powered. Keep thinking of weirder and sillier things. Think of things that are opposites: Instead of flying a kite, why not bury it? Have a cold fire or skate on hot ice. Play around with words.

This is a good chance to flex your rhyming muscles because by finding rhymes you'll think of other ideas.

If your breakfast turns into a *hippopotamus*, then what rhymes with that? How about *a lot of us*? If your toast becomes a *polar bear*, then what rhymes with that? Was the bear combing her hair, balancing on a chair, filling in a questionnaire? Was it playing a flute whilst jiving with a newt, wearing a jazzy suit? And was it cute?

Another way to do this is to start with a well known verse or nursery rhyme and then change it. Instead of Humpty Dumpty, have Mr Bean sat on the wall. Instead of a wall, how about a bridge, or a roof, or a wardrobe?

As always, when you've written your first draft read it out loud. Could you add a few good adjectives or adverbs – crazy ones of course? Can you change it to give it a good 'di dah di dah' rhythm?

Don't forget to keep the same rhythm in all the verses if you write more than one. And give each verse the same rhyme scheme – in other words, if the second and fourth lines rhyme in the first verse, make sure the same lines rhyme in the other verses.

When I Am Eighteen

When I'm eighteen
I'll dye my toes green
I'll sing all night in the park
I'll bury my kite
On the Island of Wight
And bark in the dark for a lark

When I'm twenty-nine
I'll go out to dine
On straw and eels and grunge
I'll juggle with crumpets
I'll play seven trumpets
and clean my teeth with a sponge

When I'm forty-two
I'll cook a squid stew
At the top of a mountain peak
I'll balance a hose
On the end of my nose
And I won't have a wash for a week

When I'm old as the hills
I'll look back on the thrills
That I had in my life and tell tales
Of the terrible jokes
That I played with egg yolks
on the border of England and Wales

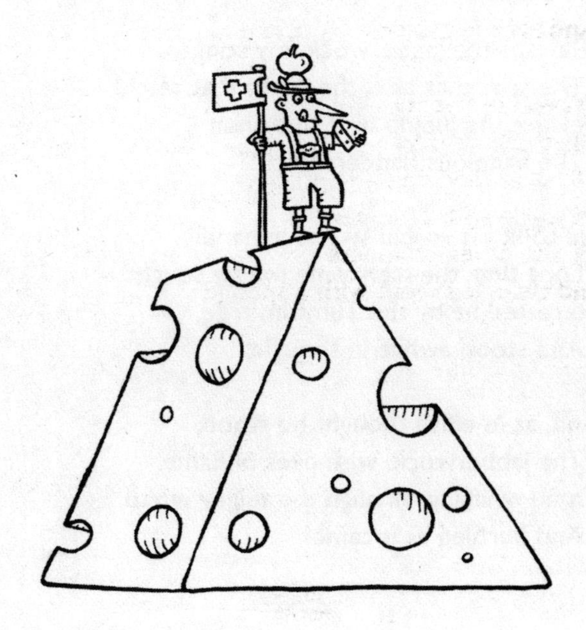

Lewis Carroll also liked to invent words. In fact, some of the words he made up have now become proper words that you can find in the dictionary – the words 'chortle' and 'galumphing' for example. They come from his poem *Jabberwocky*, which is full of nonsense words.

Jabberwocky

Lewis Carroll

'Twas brillig, and the slithy toves
  Did gyre and gimble in the wabe:
All mimsy were the borogoves,
  And the mome raths outgrabe.

"Beware the Jabberwock, my son!
  The jaws that bite, the claws that catch!
Beware the Jubjub bird, and shun
  The frumious Bandersnatch!"

He took his vorpal sword in hand:
  Long time the manxome foe he sought --
So rested he by the Tumtum tree,
  And stood awhile in thought.

And, as in uffish thought he stood,
  The Jabberwock, with eyes of flame,
Came whiffling through the tulgey wood,
  And burbled as it came!

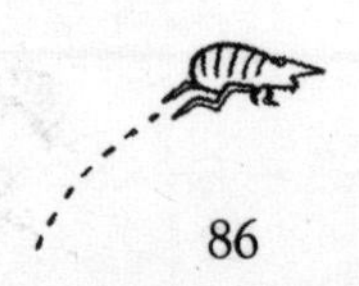

One, two! One, two! And through and through
The vorpal blade went snicker-snack!
He left it dead, and with its head
He went galumphing back.

"And, has thou slain the Jabberwock?
Come to my arms, my beamish boy!
O frabjous day! Callooh! Callay!"
He chortled in his joy.

'Twas brillig, and the slithy toves
Did gyre and gimble in the wabe;
All mimsy were the borogoves,
And the mome raths outgrabe.

This poem is different to *The Mad Gardener's Song* because it tells a story that actually makes sense – even though it's full of made-up words. It might be fun to write your own version.

For example:

'Twas Tuesday and the crabtious cook
Beheld the school canteen with mudge
She blopped the tureen with her flonk
And stirred the bubbling sludge

That's not very good is it? I bet you could do better. So good luck with your writing! And if you've written a really good rhyming poem, why not send it to me at The Poetry Zone (www.poetryzone.co.uk) – and I may even publish it!

Acknowledgements

With thanks to Gerard Benson, for his friendship and inspiration.

All poems are by Roger Stevens unless otherwise attributed. The following poems by Roger Stevens first appeared in the following anthologies and are reproduced by permission of the poet. Roger Stevens would like to thank Macmillan Children's Books for their support with this book.

'Mr Walton's On The Playground', 'Missing Monty', 'James Bond's Car', 'Michael Owen', 'Mum & Dad' in *I Did Not Eat the Goldfish* (Macmillan, 2002)

'Hill Adventure', 'Items in the Edward Lear Museum', 'Why the Bat Flies at Night', 'Forming a Band', 'How to Find Our House' in *The Monster That Ate the Universe* (Macmillan, 2004)

'Making a Poem', 'After the Summer' in *Why Otters Don't Wear Socks* (Macmillan Children's Books, 2007)

'Shoe the Blues Away' in *Vikings Don't Wear Pants* by Roger Stevens and Celia Warren (King's England Press, 2001)

'Sprint' in *Olympic Poems* by Brian Moses and Roger Stevens (Macmillan Children's Books 2012)

'Joan of Arc' in *Searching For Blue Sea Glass* by Roger Stevens (Rabbit Press, 2001)

The following poems are reproduced by kind permission of the poets or their estates:

'The Lazy Poet's Alphabet' by Gerard Benson

'The Unwed Shropshire Shepherdess' by Nick Toczek

'Spot the Fairy Tales' by James Carter, from *Journey to the Centre of my Brain* (Macmillan, 2012).

'Sir Christopher Wren' and 'Daniel Defoe' by EC Bentley reproduced with permission of Curtis Brown Group Ltd, London on behalf of the estate of EC Bentley. Copyright © EC Bentley 1905.

'Tarantella' by Hilaire Belloc from *Sonnets and Verse* (© Hilaire Belloc, 1923) reprinted by permission of Peters Fraser & Dunlop (*www.petersfraserdunlop.com*) on behalf of the Estate of Hilaire Belloc.

All efforts have been made to seek permission for copyright material, but in the event of omissions, the publisher would be pleased to hear from the copyright holders and to amend these acknowledgements in subsequent editions.